Fables and Folktales

2

Book Staff and Contributors

Kristen Kinney-Haines   *Director, English Language Arts*
Amy Rauen   *Director, Instructional Design*
Charlotte Fullerton   *Senior Media Editor*
Alane Gernon-Paulsen   *Content Specialist, Writer*
Tim Mansfield   *Writer*
Susan Raley   *Text Editor*
Tricia Battipede   *Senior Creative Design Manager, Cover Design*
Caitlin Gildrien   *Print Visual Designer, Cover Design*

At Stride, Inc. (NYSE: LRN)—formerly K12 Inc.—we are reimagining lifelong learning as a rich, deeply personal experience that prepares learners for tomorrow. Since its inception, Stride has been committed to removing barriers that impact academic equity and to providing high-quality education for anyone—particularly those in underserved communities. The company has transformed the teaching-and-learning experience for millions of people by providing innovative, high-quality, tech-enabled education solutions, curriculum, and programs directly to students, schools, the military, and enterprises in primary, secondary, and post-secondary settings. Stride is a premier provider of K–12 education for students, schools, and districts, including career-learning services through middle and high school curriculum. Providing a solution to the widening skills gap in the workplace and student loan crisis, Stride equips students with real-world skills for in-demand jobs with career learning. For adult learners, Stride delivers professional skills training in healthcare and technology, as well as staffing and talent development for Fortune 500 companies. Stride has delivered millions of courses over the past decade and serves learners in all 50 states and more than 100 countries. The company is a proud sponsor of Future of School, a nonprofit organization dedicated to closing the gap between the pace of technology and the pace of change in education. More information can be found at stridelearning.com, K12.com, destinationsacademy.com, galvanize.com, techelevator.com, and medcerts.com.

ISBN: 978-1-60153-617-4 (online book)
ISBN: 978-1-60153-610-5 (printed book)

Printed by Walsworth, St. Joseph, MI, USA, April 2022.

Fables and Folktales

Contents

Fables

Folktales

Fables

The Ant and the Dove

One day, a Dove saw a tiny Ant fall into a stream. The Ant swam and swam but could not get near the shore. The Dove, taking pity on the Ant, dropped a leaf into the water. The Ant clung to the leaf and steered it safely to the shore.

A bit later, the Ant saw a hunter getting ready to hurl a spear at the Dove. But, just as the man took aim, the Ant stung him on the heel. In pain, the man threw the spear wide, and the now fearful Dove flew off. As the Dove flew to safety, she called out her thanks to the Ant.

ONE GOOD TURN DESERVES ANOTHER.

The Grasshopper and the Ant

Characters
Grasshopper
Ant

Scene 1

Time: Summer

Place: A pleasant field

GRASSHOPPER: Ah, I am glad I have nothing to do! I can sit in the sun and be as lazy as I wish. I can watch the butterflies flit about on their pretty, bright wings, and I can listen to the humming of the bees. If I get hungry, I have juicy leaves to eat. If I get sleepy, I can hide in the grass and take a nap.

(Singing)

♫ The summertime's the time for me,

For then I'm happy as can be.

I watch the butterflies and bees;

I rest my eyes and take my ease.

I do no work the livelong day;

I pass the time in fun and play.

Oh, summertime's the time for me!

For then I'm happy as can be. ♫

An ant comes along.

Hello, Mr. Ant! Where are you going so fast?

ANT: About my work, of course. I'm a busy ant, I am.

GRASSHOPPER: Oh, you are, are you? Well, you needn't be so cross about it.

ANT: Did I speak crossly? I didn't mean to. I'm sorry. But I am very busy and can't stop to talk. *(Starting to go)*

GRASSHOPPER: Wait, wait! You can take time to talk a minute, can't you?

ANT: Why, yes, if you really have something to say.

GRASSHOPPER: Ha, ha! You make me laugh. Can't you stop a while to talk with your friends, even if they haven't much to say?

ANT: I have no time to waste.

GRASSHOPPER: Why, what are you doing today?

ANT: I am very busy getting ready for winter.

GRASSHOPPER: Getting ready for winter! Why, winter is a long way off!

ANT: It will be here soon enough.

GRASSHOPPER: Well, I don't see why you don't have a good time while you can.

ANT: But if I don't gather food for the winter now, while there is plenty of it, I shall not have anything to eat when cold weather comes.

GRASSHOPPER: Oh, you are a dull fellow! You have no fun in you.

ANT: I don't work all the time. I am busy all day, but when evening comes, I sit at home and talk with my friends.

GRASSHOPPER: Well, I don't mean to work at all in this fine weather. I'm going to have a good time.

ANT: Wait till winter comes, and we shall see who is wiser—you or I. Good-bye, I have work to do. *(Going on)*

GRASSHOPPER: What a foolish fellow that
ant is! He does nothing but work, work,
work. He doesn't have any fun at all. Well, I
don't care. I am going to have a good time.
(Singing)

♫ The summertime's the time for me,
For then I'm happy as can be.
I hop about among the flowers;
I sing and dance for hours and hours.
I care not what the ant may say;
The summertime's the time for play.
Oh, summertime's the time for me!
For then I'm happy as can be. ♫

Scene 2

Time: Winter

Place: In front of the ant's house

ANT: *(Looking out the window)* Ah, it's a cold day! I'm glad I don't have to go out. I can stay cozily at home and talk with my friends. I have plenty of food, too, so I have nothing to do through the winter but have a good time.

The grasshopper comes along. He looks thin and hungry. His clothes are old and ragged. He stops in front of the ant's house.

GRASSHOPPER: Oh, Mr. Ant, won't you please give me something to eat?

ANT: Why, Mr. Grasshopper, is that you? I hardly knew you. You are not looking very well.

GRASSHOPPER: No, no! I'm afraid not. I'm not feeling well, either.

ANT: Why, what's the matter?

GRASSHOPPER: I am hungry. Won't you please give me something to eat?

ANT: Something to eat! Why, what did you do all summer?

GRASSHOPPER: I sang and played all summer. I had plenty of food then. Now it is cold, and there is nothing to eat.

ANT: Oh, you lazy fellow! You sang and played all summer, while the rest of us were busy storing up food for the winter. Now that it is cold and there is no food, you ask us to feed you. Take this grain, but do not ask again. You shall get no more from me.

GRASSHOPPER: Ah, me! Why did I not work as the ant did, and store up food while there was still food to get?

(Singing sadly)

♫ I did no work all summer long.

And now I know that I was wrong.

It isn't right for me to play

While the ants work hard all day.

Next time I'll work as well as dance,

Then I'll be ready, like the ants. ♫

WORK HARD TODAY SO YOU'RE READY FOR TOMORROW. ✎

The Lion and the Fox

A lion who was old and weak could not go out to hunt for food. He went into his den and made believe that he was very sick.

Many animals went into the den to look at him. When they came near, he caught them and ate them.

After a great many had been caught in this way, a fox came along. He sat down outside the den and asked the lion how he was.

The lion said that he was very sick, and he begged the fox to come in and see him.

"I would," said the fox, "but I notice that all the footprints point into your den, and that none point out."

LEARN FROM THE MISTAKES OF OTHERS. ༡

The Hound and the Hare

A Hound startled a Hare near the woods and began to chase him. As the Hare dashed back and forth, the Hound played a game. At first, she bit him with her teeth as if she would end his life. Then she tumbled the Hare in the grass as if playing with another dog.

Finally, not knowing whether he would be eaten or be the Hound's friend, the Hare stopped running.

He said, "Hound, I wish you would act truthfully with me. If you are my friend, why do you bite me? And if you are my enemy, why do you play with me?"

SHE IS NO FRIEND WHO PLAYS DOUBLE. ⟡

Folktales

The Three Wishes

There was once a poor woman who worked all day in the forest. She gathered great bundles of sticks and sold them in the village.

One day, she had very bad luck indeed. No one wanted to buy any of her sticks. When the night came, she had not a cent to take home to her children.

"Dear me!" said the poor woman. "No supper for us tonight!"

Just then, she heard a strange noise in the dead leaves near the path. She turned to look and saw a rabbit caught in a trap.

"Here is supper!" cried the old woman and ran to the trap.

"If you spare me," cried the rabbit, "I will grant the first three wishes made by you or your children."

"That is better than one supper," said the
woman, and she freed the rabbit.

The rabbit ran off into the forest, and the
happy woman hurried home to tell the good
news to her children.

They met her at the door. "What have you
brought us for supper?" they asked.

"Nothing!" said the woman.

"Then there is nothing to eat," they all
wailed. The youngest cried, "Oh I wish I had a
big cake to eat!"

At once a giant cake appeared on the table. Such a large cake had never been seen!

"Child, child! What have you done?" cried the woman. "We had three wishes! You have used one of them for a cake. Oh, I wish it were hung from your nose!"

As she spoke, the cake rose slowly and stuck to the child's nose. Everyone was shocked! The poor woman pulled, but the cake stuck fast to the child's nose.

"Oh dear! Oh dear! Take it away! Take it away!" cried the child, but there it stayed.

"Never mind!" said the oldest child. "We have one more wish. Let us ask for all the riches in the world!"

"But my nose! My nose!" cried the youngest.

"Hush!" said the middle child, but the little one would not hush.

Then the woman became angry. "Away with the cake!" she shouted. "I wish it would fly up the chimney!"

Before anyone knew it, the big cake rolled from its place on the child's nose and then flew up the chimney. A few crumbs rattled in the ashes, and that was the end of the three wishes. ❧

The Fisherman and His Wife

A fisherman and his wife lived in a little old house by the sea. Every day the fisherman went down to the sea to fish. Every day his wife cooked the fish for dinner. One day, when he threw in his line, it suddenly became very heavy. He pulled and pulled, and out flopped a big fish. The fisherman said to himself, "This is too big for my wife and me. We will invite our friends to dinner."

But the fish said, "Oh, do not eat me. Put me back into the sea, and you shall have whatever you wish."

The fisherman quickly threw the fish back into the sea. "Who would eat a talking fish!" he said.

"Go back to your friends, and I will throw my line for another fish." When he went back to his house, he told his wife about the talking fish.

"What a goose you are!" she said angrily. "Why did you not ask for something? Go back and ask him to change this shabby old house into a pretty cottage."

The fisherman walked slowly back to the sea. The water looked all yellow and green. The fisherman called:

> "Oh, Man of the Sea,
> Come listen to me,
> For Ilsa, my wife,
> The love of my life,
> Hath sent me to ask a gift
> Of thee!"

The fish came swimming up to him.

"My wife wishes to live in a pretty little cottage," said the fisherman.

"Go home," said the fish. "She is in the cottage already."

The fisherman went home. Sure enough, there was his wife standing at the door of a pretty little cottage. The fisherman could hardly believe his eyes. There was a little garden in front and a chicken yard at the back.

"Ah! Now you shall be happy," said the fisherman.

And she was happy—for a week.

Then one day the wife said, "Husband, I am tired of this little cottage. It is too small. I wish to live in a big stone castle. Go to the fish and ask for one."

The fisherman walked slowly down to the sea. The water was dark, and the sun did not shine. The fisherman called:

> "Oh, Man of the Sea,
> Come listen to me,
> For Ilsa, my wife,
> The love of my life,
> Hath sent me to ask a gift
> Of thee!"

The fish came swimming up to him.

"My wife wishes to live in a big stone castle," said the fisherman.

"Go home," said the fish. "She is in the castle already."

The fisherman went home. Sure enough, there was a great stone castle. When the fisherman came to the door, it was opened by a servant, who made a low bow. Inside the castle, he found more servants. And in the

great hall, he saw his wife. She was walking up and down, with her head in the air.

The fisherman rubbed his eyes and looked again. He saw golden chairs and tables and fine things to eat. He thought it must all be a dream.

"Wake up!" said his wife. "What are you staring at?"

"How grand it is!" said the fisherman. "Now you will be happy."

And happy she was—for a day.

The next morning, before the sun was up, Ilsa called to the fisherman, "Husband, go to the fish at once and tell him I wish to be queen of all the land."

The fisherman walked very slowly to the sea. The water was black, and the waves rolled high. He called in a loud voice:

> "Oh, Man of the Sea,
> Come listen to me,
> For Ilsa, my wife,
> The love of my life,
> Hath sent me to ask a gift
> Of thee!"

When the fish came swimming up to him, the fisherman said, "My wife desires to be queen of all the land."

"She is already queen," said the fish.

The fisherman hurried home and found his wife on a throne of gold and diamonds.

She had a golden crown on her head, and
wore a silk dress with a long train.

"Wife, wife, now you shall be happy," he said.

And happy she was—for an hour.

Then she said, "I am queen, and you must
do as I wish. I order you to go to the fish and
tell him that I desire the power to make the sun
and the moon rise and set whenever I choose."

The fisherman was very sad as he walked to the sea. The sky was full of black clouds. The waves were as high as hills. The thunder crashed, and the fisherman had to shout:

> "Oh, Man of the Sea,
> Come listen to me,
> For Ilsa, my wife,
> The love of my life,
> Hath sent me to ask a gift
> Of thee!"

The fish rose on the top of a wave.

The fisherman said, "My wife wishes the power to make the sun and moon rise and set whenever she chooses."

"Go to your little old house," said the fish. "Remain there and be content."

And there you will find the fisherman and his wife to this very day. ❧

The Foolish Goose

Characters
Gray Goose
Wise Old Crow
White Crane
Brownie Hen
a Farmer

Time: One bright morning

Place: A big road

Gray Goose goes walking down the road, with a bag of corn—very proud and happy. He meets Wise Old Crow.

WISE OLD CROW: Good morning, Gray Goose! What a heavy bag you have there! It is too much for you to carry alone. Let me help you.

GRAY GOOSE: Oh, no! It is a big bag of corn, but I can carry it without any help.

WISE OLD CROW: Oh, well, I just wanted to help you as a friend. How long do you think your bag of corn will last you? I can tell you of a plan to make a little corn go a long way.

GRAY GOOSE: What is your plan? Tell me how to make my corn go a long way, Wise Old Crow.

He puts down his bag of corn in the road.

WISE OLD CROW: First, you must spread your corn out on the ground, so that we can count it. Then you count on one side, and I will count on the other side.

Gray Goose takes some of the corn out of the bag and spreads it on the ground.

GRAY GOOSE: *(Counting)* One, two, three, four, five, six, seven, eight, nine—

WISE OLD CROW: *(Eating a kernel of corn each time he counts)* One, two, three, four, five, six, seven, eight, nine—

GRAY GOOSE: *(Looking up)* What are you doing, Wise Old Crow? Stop eating my corn!

WISE OLD CROW: *(As he flies away, laughing)* Caw! Caw! Caw! I told you that I knew a plan to make a little corn go a long way!

Gray Goose picks up his bag of corn, which is not so heavy now, and goes along the road. After a while, he meets White Crane.

WHITE CRANE: Good morning, Gray Goose! What do you have in your bag?

GRAY GOOSE: Oh, that is some of the best corn in the world.

WHITE CRANE: Is that all? You carry it with such care that I thought it must be pearls or diamonds.

GRAY GOOSE: No, I've never seen any pearls or diamonds. I should like very much to see such sights!

WHITE CRANE: Well, just swim out to that big rock in the lake over there. The bottom of the lake is covered with beautiful pearls and diamonds. I will keep your corn for you.

Gray Goose swims out to see the wonderful sights. While he is gone, White Crane eats nearly all of the corn. Gray Goose cannot see any pearls or diamonds on the bottom of the lake. When he starts back, he sees White Crane eating the corn.

GRAY GOOSE: Get away from my corn, White Crane! Get away from my corn!

WHITE CRANE: *(As he flies off, laughing)* I told you that I would keep your corn for you, Gray Goose!

Gray Goose picks up the little corn that is left and goes down the road. After a while, he meets Brownie Hen and her ten chicks.

BROWNIE HEN: What have you got in that little bag, Gray Goose?

GRAY GOOSE: Oh, just a few kernels of corn. I had a big bagful, but White Crane ate most of it while I was looking for pearls and diamonds! I like to see strange sights.

BROWNIE HEN: Well, if you like to see strange sights, throw your corn upon the road and see what happens.

GRAY GOOSE: No, indeed! I know well enough what would happen! Your ten little chicks would eat every kernel of it.

BROWNIE HEN: No, no, Gray Goose! My chicks will not steal your corn. Throw some of it upon the road. If my little ones eat a single kernel, I will give you ten white eggs.

GRAY GOOSE: All right! I agree to that.

He throws down some corn. The chicks run toward it. But before they can eat it, Brownie Hen makes a noise like a hawk. The chicks run away, and Brownie Hen eats the corn.

BROWNIE HEN: I told you that my chicks would not eat your corn, Gray Goose!

Gray Goose goes on until he meets a farmer.

FARMER: What is in your bag, Gray Goose?

GRAY GOOSE: *(Sadly)* Only a few kernels of corn. My bag grows smaller and smaller. I wish I could make it grow bigger and bigger!

FARMER: Why don't you put the corn in the ground? Then it will grow, and you will always have plenty to eat.

GRAY GOOSE: I will do as you say, Farmer.

He plants it, and later the corn begins to grow. For every kernel he planted, Gray Goose has hundreds of kernels!

GRAY GOOSE: At last I have found a way to make my bag of corn grow bigger and bigger instead of smaller and smaller!

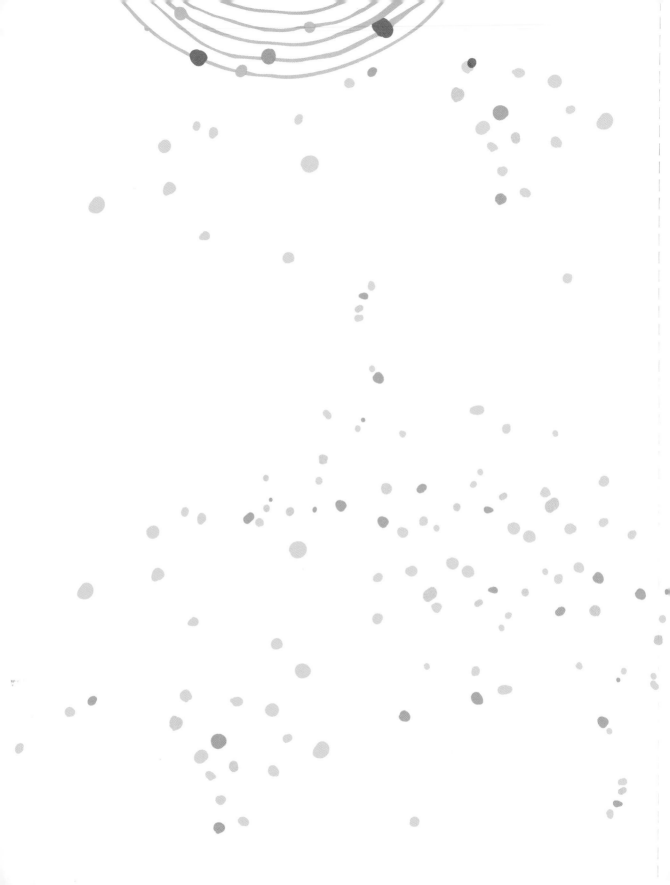